Really Useful
Engines
Activity Book

"Peep! Peep!" Here comes Thomas.
What a Really Useful Engine he is!

Colour in Thomas, using the small picture to help you.

How many pictures of Thomas, Bertie, The Fat Controller and Harold can you see?

These pictures look the same, but 5 things are different in picture 2.

Look carefully. Can you spot them all?

Here comes James, the splendid red engine.
Can you match the picture of James to the correct shadow?

Some of Thomas' friends have names which start with the same letter.

Draw lines to match them to each other.

Bulstrode

Harold

Terence

Bertie

Henry

Trevor

The platform is very busy and crowded.

How many mail bags can you see in the picture?
How many parcels? And how many birds?

There are

mail bags.

There are

birds.

There are

parcels.

One of these pictures of the engines is different from the rest.
Can you spot the odd one out?

Answer: picture 6 is the odd one out – Gordon's steam is missing.

Find two pictures of Thomas that are exactly the same.

Then colour them in.

James is running low on fuel!

Which track should he take to reach the coal hopper?

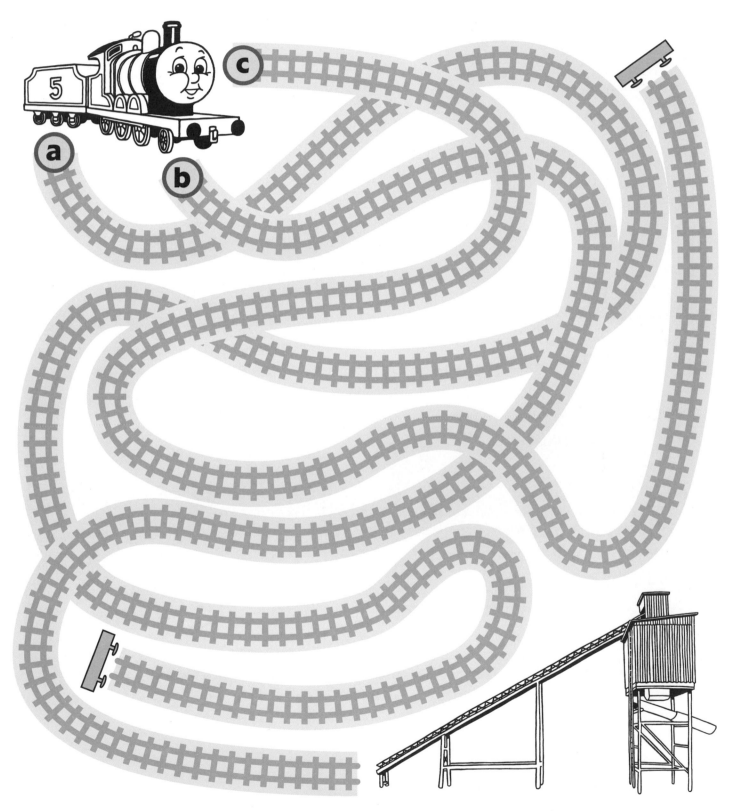

Thomas is steaming through the countryside.

How many people can you count in the picture?

There are ☐ people.

How many pictures of each engine can you see?

Do you know all their names?

Thomas   **Toby**   **Douglas**   **Percy**

Here are some of Thomas' friends.

Draw lines to match them with their names.

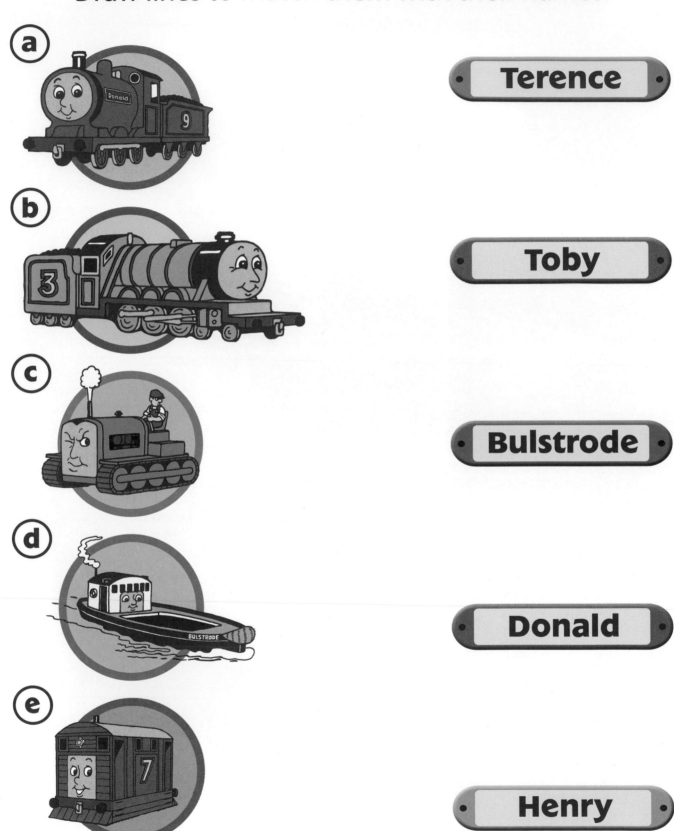

a

Terence

b

Toby

c

Bulstrode

d

Donald

e

Henry

Which of these useful machines need tracks to help them move about?

Circle them, then check your answers.

Edward

Trevor

Terence

Bertie

Harold

Thomas

Answer: Thomas and Edward need tracks.

Edward and Trevor are both steaming through Sodor!

Colour in this picture as neatly as you can.
You can use the picture opposite as a guide.

Draw lines to match the words to Thomas' body.

wheels

buffers

Driver's cab

funnel

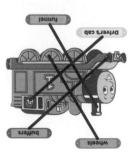

Thomas and Gordon are having a rest.

These pictures look the same, but 5 things are different in picture 2. Look carefully. Can you spot them all?

Donald's Driver needs to reach him.

Show him the quickest way through the maze.

START

FINISH

Answer:

Draw lines to match the engines to their colours.

Then colour them in.

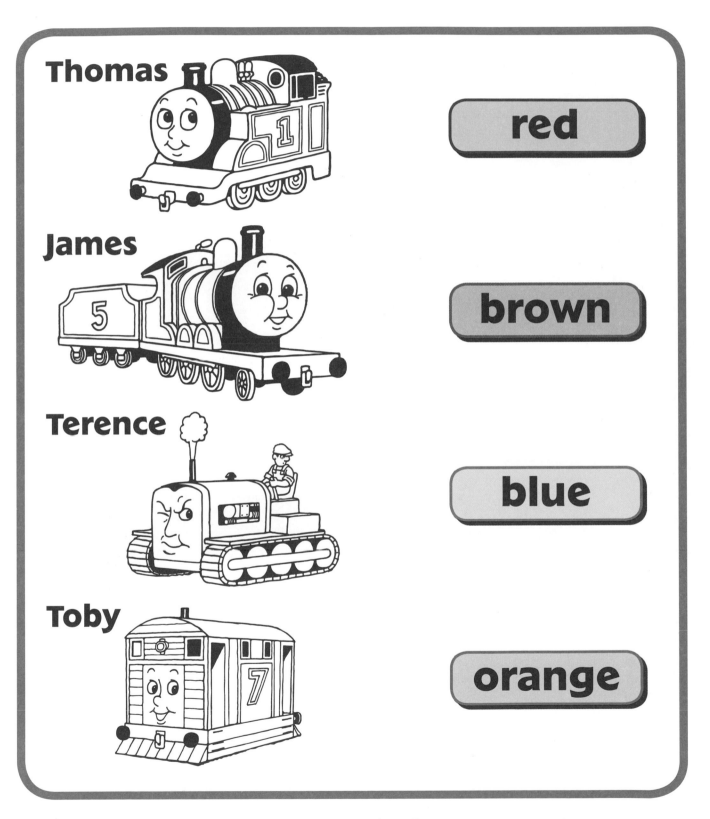

Thomas

James

Terence

Toby

red

brown

blue

orange

Draw over the lines to copy the picture of Bertie square by square.

Now colour in your picture.

One of these pictures of Terence is different from the rest.

Can you spot the odd one out?

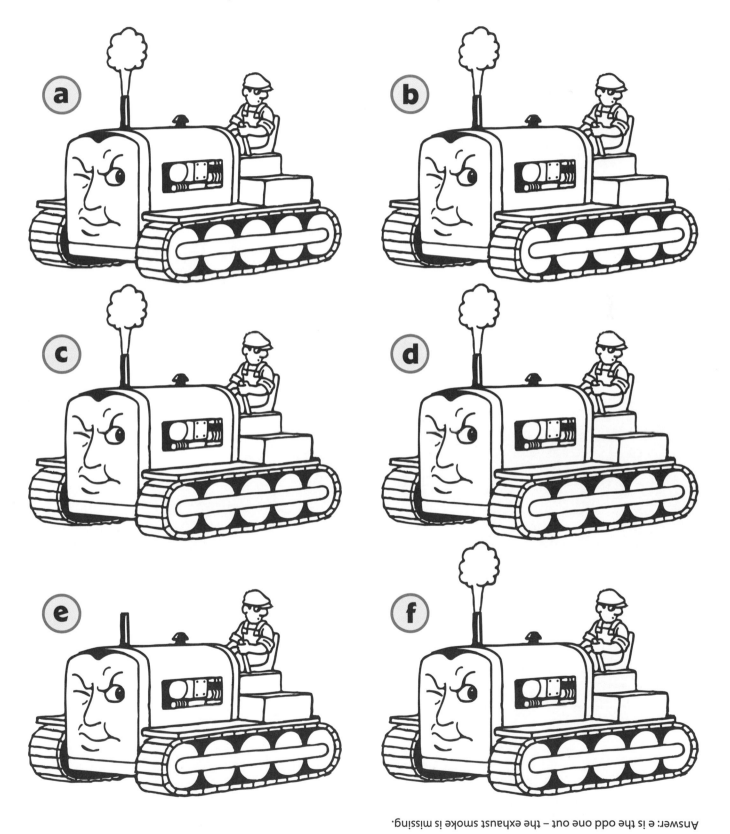

The Fat Controller is very happy with Thomas because he is a Really Useful Engine!

Colour the picture in as neatly as you can.